The Pride Street Crew
1
It's Not The Winning

Mike Wilson

Published in association with
The Basic Skills Agency

Acknowledgements
Cover: Stuart Williams
Illustrations: Jim Eldridge

Orders: please contact Bookpoint Ltd, 39 Milton Park, Abingdon, Oxon OX14 4TD. Telephone: (44) 01235 400414, Fax: (44) 01235 400454. Lines are open from 9.00–6.00, Monday to Saturday, with a 24 hour message answering service. Email address: orders@bookpoint.co.uk

British Library Cataloguing in Publication Data
A catalogue record for this title is available from The British Library

ISBN 0 340 74709 9

First published 1999
Impression number   10 9 8 7 6 5 4 3 2 1
Year   2004 2003 2002 2001 2000 1999

Typeset by Fakenham Photosetting Ltd, Fakenham, Norfolk
Printed in Great Britain for Hodder & Stoughton Educational, a division of Hodder Headline Plc, 338 Euston Road, London NW1 3BH by Athenaeum Press, Gateshead, Tyne & Wear.

JOHN / BONE

WESLEY / TALL

LUKE / SKY

SIMON / CUSTARD

CARL / SPOT

Say hello
to the Pride Street Crew.

We all live on
the same street.
Pride Street.

We're not much of a gang.
We don't do
what real gangs do.
We just hang around together
after school.

We play football
in the park.
Then we just hang about,
and call each other names.

One time,
we found a dead cat.

One time,
we found a tramp's trousers.

But it isn't always
that much fun.

Say hello to the Crew.

Bone's real name
is John Bell.

Bone got his name
when he was ten.
He fell badly
when he was playing football.

He broke his leg.

Bone lay on the grass.
He was trying
not to move.
Trying not to cry.

We all stood there,
looking.
You could see
the white bone,
sticking out.

Tall's real name
is Wesley.

By the time he was 14,
he was 1 metre 80.

That's why
we call him Tall.

Custard's real name
is Simon Dodds.

At dinner time at school,
we wait.
He puts custard
in his mouth.

Then we shout,
'CUSTARD!'
He starts to laugh.
The custard comes
down his nose!

It works
with gravy too.

Spot's real name
is Carl.
His Dad is well off.

Carl was the first boy
in our year
to have a bike.
And a Playstation.

And spots.

And I'm Luke,
the good-looking one.

The gang all call me Sky
for short.

Can you work out
what that is short for?

This is how
the Pride Street Crew began.

It was at school.
Mr Baxter told us about
the Five-a-Side Cup.

The Five-a-Side Cup
was on the next Saturday.
They wanted teams.

16

'Let's make a five-a-side team!'
I said to Tall.
'You and me, and Bone
and Custard and Spot.
That makes five.
Let's go in
for the Five-a-Side Cup!'

'Yes,' said Tall,
'but we're no good.'

'That don't matter!' I said.
'It will be fun!'

'I don't care if we win or lose,'
I went on.
'My Dad says –
it's not the winning.
It's the taking part!'

The new team had
to have a name.
And that is how
the Pride Street Crew began.

The next Saturday
we went to the Five-a-Side Cup.

It was big.
There were about
30 other teams.

All the other teams
were older than us.
All the other teams
had managers –
men in suits
with mobile phones.

All the other teams
had shirts with their names on.
Our shirts had holes in.
Our shirts were not
all the same colour.

We had two games.
We lost one 9–0.
We lost the other one 11–1.
Then we were out of the Cup.

We did get one goal.
But even that
was an own goal
by the other team.
They said they felt sorry for us.
So they let one in.

After that,
the Pride Street Crew
was a bit of a joke.

At school,
boys laughed at us.
Girls laughed at us.
Even Mr Baxter laughed at us.

But we didn't mind.

Win or lose,
it was fun.

As my Dad says:
It's not the winning.

It's the taking apart.

If you have enjoyed reading about the Pride Street Crew, you may be interested in other books in the *Livewire* series:

Plays
Beach Babe
A Great Day Out!
Spooky!
Mobile Phoney
Mine Shaft
Sleeping Rough
Clubbing

Chillers
The Cellar
Second Sight
The Rocking Chair
Invisible Ink
Hit and Run
Bargain with a Stranger
The Singer
The Fetch
Life Sentence